Bright Ideas

for Early Years

Science Activities

Max de Bóo

Published by Scholastic Publications Ltd,
Villiers House, Clarendon Avenue,
Leamington Spa, Warwickshire CV32 5PR.

© 1990 Scholastic Publications Ltd
Reprinted 1991, 1992, 1993, 1994

Written by Max de Bóo
Edited by Jane Bishop
Sub-edited by Catherine Baker
Designed by Sue Limb
Illustrations by Helen Herbert
Cover photograph by Martyn Chillmaid

Artwork by Liz Preece,
Castle Graphics, Kenilworth
Printed in Great Britain by
The Alden Press Ltd, Oxford

Photographs by Richard Butchins (pages
5, 9, 27 and 55), Bob Bray (page 17),
Terry Williams (pages 37 and 67), Keith
Hawkins (page 45) and Derek Dryland
(page 75).

British Library Cataloguing in Publication Data
De Boo, Max
    Science activities.
    1. Science
    I. Title   II. Series
    500

    ISBN 0 590 76230 3

Contents

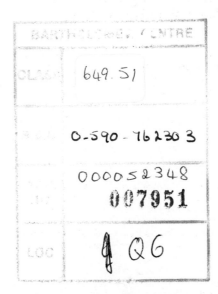

Acknowledgements

Like most primary teachers I have been eclectic in my approach, interlacing the best ideas I could find with my own responses to the children's stimuli. I owe much to many of the colleagues I have had the privilege of working with in Barnet, Haringey and Essex.
Thank you.

Ideas on pages 10, 14, 43, 46, 62, 90 originally came from *Child Education* magazine.

Introduction

The content of this book has been prepared with reference to the broad science curriculum, thinking also of the experiences and everyday events that are relevant to most of our three-to-six-year-olds, and the skills we are trying to encourage in them. The fundamental skills of observation and communication need more space than it is possible to give them here, but I have tried to show in the questioning technique how *any* activity can be brought into a scientific focus by asking questions such as 'What does it look like?'; 'How big is it?'; 'What is it doing?'.

Questions that ask for predictions give us vital clues to the children's prior experience and existing concepts and ideas. They also provide a positive reference point for reflection when the activity has been concluded. Try to accept all predictions and conclusions — they are always logical to the children. If no opportunity arises to help them modify their opinion at that stage, the response is, 'It certainly looks like that, doesn't it?'.

Children bring their own ideas with them, and with encouragement and appreciation they soon get into the habit of suggesting investigations, materials, methods of building etc. It is always exciting to see how the creativity and lateral thinking of young children can apply to practical activities.

Resources on show

The resources suggested in 'What you need' should be fairly easily accessible. Young children also need good science equipment like magnets, lenses and electricity kits — they can and do use these with confidence and growing understanding. If things are not available, start collecting and ordering them, and meanwhile borrow some, perhaps from a science centre or nearby senior school. A good supply of everyday junk materials is also absolutely essential.

With each activity I would suggest having the main resource visible — they will inspire the children's ingenuity. 'Controlling the variables' at this age is best done or guided by the teacher; for example, in comparative investigations keep the number of objects to four, five or six, with clearly identifiable similarities and differences.

I recommend starting with a real object or problem to solve — the children's imagination and ideas take off very quickly.

Group sizes will depend on staffing, the nature of the activity and, most of all, the resources. Some of the activities require the teacher to work closely with the children, whereas others may be done by groups of children working together, perhaps on a structure, with intermittent support from the teacher. The suggestions given in this book try to reflect this, some activities beginning with a lot of teacher-involvement before moving on to work in smaller groups.

Concern is sometimes expressed about the other children 'seeing what the first group is doing'. I don't think this is too important; the practical nature of the activity will always catch their enthusiasm anyway. The 'noise' associated with active behaviour and conversation is usually a productive sound.

Objectives and preparation

In writing the objectives I have tried to show how simple classroom activities give the children experience of forces, materials, the living world, energy etc. Some activities are brief, others are more extended, and the time allocated may vary accordingly. In most cases the 'answers' are not supplied, as there is often more than one conclusion and all are equally satisfactory.

I have implied in certain activities that the teacher may have to do some preparation, such as cutting out, or 'helping'. There is a place for encouraging the manipulative skills, but it is equally important to encourage investigation and understanding. In some cases a child's energy could be unnecessarily diverted if there is considerable work to be done before the real enquiry. Sometimes I have also suggested work that can be done with less teacher interaction, after the main activity, since time needs to be found to investigate with another group of children or extend work elsewhere in the classroom.

The follow-up activities vary, but they are aimed at achieving one or more of the following objectives:
- extending experience of a scientific idea or concept;
- developing and applying scientific ideas in cross-curricular activities;
- encouraging the children's skills in language and mathematics;

- creating an exciting classroom environment that will stimulate further thought and investigation;
- giving demonstrable evidence, other than written records, of the children's learning experiences.

Writing and reading about their discoveries, questions and surprises is a wonderful use of literacy skills – whether the writing is done by the children themselves or by the teacher. Sometimes no record is necessary – the activity and discussion are sufficient.

Each activity in this book has a reference to its National Curriculum applications. As all the activities are designed for the early years, the Levels are almost entirely 1–3. Occasionally there are no relevant Statements of Attainment at these levels such as Exploration of weather, Electrical conductivity, Balancing forces in structures, or Measuring time. The programmes of study are your best guide.

All the ideas involve AT1, and strand references are omitted as all three are included. There may be a particular emphasis on applying science in a 'Design and make' activity, which would make it useful for tying in with the National Curriculum for Design and Technology. Where this is so the letters D&M appear with the Attainment Target references.

Questions and answers

The suggested 'Questions' after an activity are an outline of how one might get information about the children's increasing understanding. Some of this will be apparent during the investigation, and some will be articulated later. These are not structured 'assessment' questions, but they will help to identify areas of confusion and suggest ways to clarify

and extend understanding. It is best not to expect too much of the children, or to underestimate the value of the experience if there is little oral feedback. Much learning gets stored for reflection and for matching up with other experiences. Keep an open mind – trust your children and your own professionalism (or parental know-how if using this book at home).

If Einstein is right, we are *all* scientists, for we are all 'trying to make sense of ourselves and our world'. We are involved in the adventure as much as the children are, and we will learn too when we explore our world with the children in a scientific way.

Ourselves

Chapter one

Helping children to develop an awareness of themselves means giving them opportunities to explore their senses, observe their features and limbs and think about their place in the family.

The youngest children will have learned the difference between 'me' and 'not-me'; now they need to look at the similarities and differences between themselves and other people. Sometimes the similarities need emphasising — we are all human beings, with the same needs and emotions, and there is a lovely feeling of 'belonging' when these topics are discussed in class. Differences in hair colour and teeth, feet and hand size will all stimulate classification and ordering skills, with measurement in arbitrary units and comparative statements.

Encouraging these observations will call for materials and equipment for self-analysis — plenty of good mirrors and hand lenses, a camera, a tape-recorder and access to a photocopier.

Looking in mirrors

Objective
To encourage self-observation using mirrors.

What you need
Mirrors (including a full-length one), paper, paints, brushes, glass cloth or tea-towel for cleaning the mirrors, pencils, crayons, aluminium foil, shoe-boxes, lemonade bottles, shiny metal spoons.

What to do
Let the children look at themselves in a full-length mirror. What colour is their hair? Their skin? Their eyes? Their clothes? Can they touch their mirror-nose? Their mirror-hands? What happens to their mirror self if they smile? If they wave?

Follow-up
• Where else can they see their own reflection? Try water, glass and metal.
• Wrap aluminium foil taut, with the fewest wrinkles possible, around a bottle or across a shoe-box and stick down tightly. Let the children look at themselves in these. What do they notice?
• Set up a mirror table with mirrors stuck vertically in Plasticine. Angle some of them together and put small animals or objects in front for the children to observe their images.
• In PE, do mirroring movements in pairs.
• Use a projector lamp to make silhouettes.

Questions
Where do we put the mirrors in our houses? In school? Why do we put them there?

AT1, AT2 (i/ii), AT4 (iv)

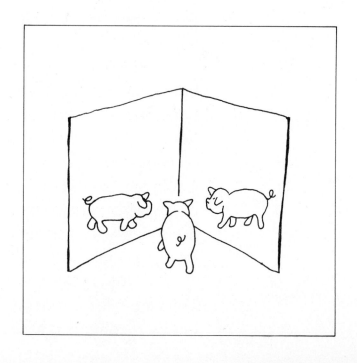

Teeth

Objectives
To observe ourselves and our teeth.

What you need
Mirrors, both straight and angled, fresh food eg apple, cheese and banana, new Plasticine.

What to do
Let the children use the mirrors to look closely at their teeth. Are all our teeth the same? What do they feel like with our tongues?

What marks do they make when we bite with them? Let the children make bite marks in the cheese, the fruit and the Plasticine.

Draw pictures of people and animals showing their teeth.

Follow-up
• Make the home corner into a dentist's surgery or a chemist's shop with varieties of toothpaste for sale.
• Find information books illustrating human teeth, or animals with biting, tearing and chewing teeth.
• Make plaster casts of the teeth impressions in the Plasticine.
• Ask a friendly dentist for old casts of teeth.

Questions
Can the children guess what teeth are made of? Why do we need to take care of our teeth and clean them every day?

AT1, AT2 (i/ii)

Hands

Objective
To encourage close observation of our hands.

What you need
Access to a photocopier, paints and paper.

What to do
Ask the children to observe their hands closely, both on the front and on the back.

Put the photocopier on to the lightest setting and take copies of the children's hands (a jacket over the edge will cut out the light flash).

Look at the photocopies and compare them. Is it possible to see which parts of the hand were pressed against the glass?

Set up a table with equipment for hand and finger-painting, and take prints.

Follow-up
• Make hand-prints, cut them out and assemble as a tree, a peacock, or some flowers.
• Make a collection of mittens and gloves for measuring and displaying.
• Make a class book with children's comments — 'My hands can . . .'.
• Play hand games such as 'Incey Wincey Spider'.
• Measure things with handspans.

Questions
What could we not do if we had no hands? What does it feel like when we hold hands with Mum, Dad or friends?

AT1, AT2 (i/ii), AT4 (iv)

Touch

Objective
To encourage observation by touching and feeling.

What you need
A variety of materials eg fur fabric, rough coconut matting, smooth wood, a metal tray, a rubber car mat, hessian, corrugated paper.

What to do
Let the children feel the different materials.

How do their fingers and hands know which is which? Can they tell with their eyes closed? Can they feel with their bare feet? With their socks on?

Which materials feel nicest to touch? Which ones feel uncomfortable?

Follow-up
• Provide a variety of fabrics to make a textured pattern or picture.
• Make a collection of different objects to display and feel.
• Make a 'feely bag' and let the children guess the hidden objects.

Questions
Why are some things made especially prickly? Can the children think of leaves or animals that have prickles?

AT1, AT2 (ii), AT3 (i)

13

Feet

Objective
To observe our feet.

What you need
Trays of fairly thick paint, newspaper, an old wet towel, two or three clean dry towels, bowls of warm soapy water, sugar paper or frieze paper, and with the youngest children another adult helper.

What to do
Before the children come in, do a shoe-print of your own. Can the children guess whose it is? Check against your shoe.

What kind of prints would their shoes make? Make shoe-prints (clean afterwards on the old towel) and look at the shapes and patterns.

Let the children make footprints with their bare feet. Are they all the same? Who has curly toes? Who has straight toes?

Follow-up
• Cut out some of the bare footprints and put them over the shoe-prints. Do they fit? If not, can the children suggest why?
• Play gripping games with bare feet, and focus on footwork in PE.
• Make printing blocks with polystyrene pieces cut out and stuck or stapled on to blocks of wood, to make shoe-shapes or animal footprints.
• Look out for footprints in mud or snow.

Questions
Which parts of our feet are best for gripping?
What are babies' feet like?

AT1, AT2 (i/ii)

Listening

Objective
To encourage observation by listening.

What you need
Audio tape recorder, a variety of sound-makers eg keys, tin cans, milk bottles, percussion instruments etc.

What to do
Choose a few sounds to 'play' to the children. Can they say what the sounds are like? What else do they remind them of?

Can they recognise them with their eyes closed, or hidden behind a screen?

Can they guess where the sound is coming from with their eyes closed? (Move around the room.)

Tape record sounds with and without the children – in the classroom, around the school and at home – and let the children listen, describe and identify them.

Follow-up
● Look at each other's ears – what do they look like? Older children could draw a partner's ear.
● Listen to sounds tapped through the radiator pipes, speak through a sugar paper 'megaphone', or talk into a tin or pot.

Questions
What does it feel like when a noise is very loud? (NB Safety – beware of subjecting children's ears to loud noises.) Which sounds make us feel scared? Which make us feel excited?

AT1, AT2 (i/ii), AT4 (iv)

Smelling

Objective
To encourage observation by smelling.

What you need
Aromatic objects or foods eg a rose, mint leaves, Marmite, honey, an orange, and one or two non-aromatic objects, such as a pencil, paper, tins or boxes.

What to do
Let the children smell the objects and describe them. Put the aromatic things into tins to conceal them and let the children smell them again. Can they guess which one is which?

Increase the number of objects to about ten and ask the children to sort them according to whether they like or dislike the smell, whether it is strong or faint, or any other criteria they can think of.

Follow-up
• Make sets of likes and dislikes.
• Give the children mirrors with which to look at their noses (older children could draw them).
• Go for a 'smelly' walk around the school, nearby shops or a park. (NB — emphasise caution with unknown items.)
• Make a display table of things to smell.

Questions
How far away can we smell the strong smells?
What else are noses used for?

AT1, AT2 (ii), AT3 (i)

Other living things

Chapter two

Observation of plant and animal life will help to give the children a perspective on the living world and encourage sensitivity towards their environment. Studies in this area will develop skills of observation and communication, and attitudes of curiosity, co-operation and a willingness to appraise evidence.

Apart from easy access to tools and equipment for collecting and observing, the single biggest factor in developing this area will be direct contact with the living environment.

Start with a visit to look, listen, touch and smell the local environment. Collect some interesting items to take back to school. (Remember to return any creatures to their natural habitat as soon as possible.) Sort and classify the materials by colour, size, and whether they are shiny or dull, prickly or smooth. Photograph the sets, draw around the objects or display them.

Trees

Objective
To observe the detail and structure of tree bark by making a plaster cast.

What you need
A few accessible trees, Plasticine, bowl, spoon, plaster of Paris, newspaper, tray, water.

What to do
Roll or press out the Plasticine into a thick sheet approximately 25cm by 20cm. Press this firmly on to the bark of a nearby tree. Peel off. Put this 'print' upwards on newspaper in a tray and add some little Plasticine walls around the edge to prevent the plaster overflowing the tray.

Mix the plaster to a thick creamy consistency, pour into the mould and leave to set. Feel the plaster gently at regular intervals while it is setting. What do the children notice? When the plaster is set, gently peel off the Plasticine.

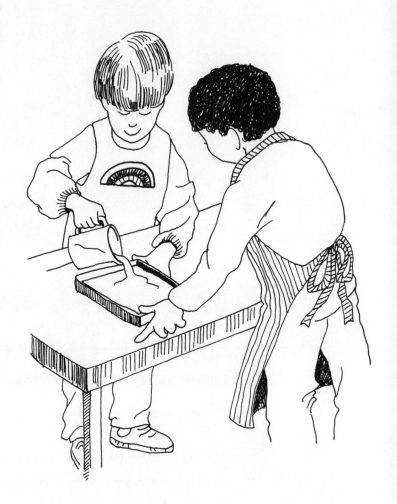

Follow-up
• Paint the plaster cast. Display it with leaves, books and other 'tree products'.
• Arrange a leaf or leaves in the bottom of a saucer. Fold a loop of string over the edge, then fill the saucer with plaster. These will make interesting wall plaques if painted and varnished.
• Can the children think of other possible plaster casts?

Questions
Can the children suggest why tree bark needs to be so thick?
What do they think the plaster is made of that makes it go so hard? Can they think of other ways of making things set solid?

AT1, AT2 (i/ii), AT3 (i)

Seeds

Objective
To observe seeds carefully.

What you need
A variety of seeds eg cress, sweet pea, nasturtium, cabbage, sunflower, grass, mung beans, green bean seeds, card, sticky tape, magnifying glasses.

What to do
Stick a few of each sort of seed on to cards – make two cards for each type of seed, one with the name on it and one without. Mix them all up. Can the children match the un-named cards with the named ones? Can they match them with their packets (tops stuck down)? Add more seed varieties to the game. Use the magnifying glasses for close observation.

Follow-up
• Give the children paper packets and ask them to draw pictures of a plant or flower on the front. Children with writing skills could write instructions for growing the plants on the back of the packet.
• Fill the packets with real seeds, or little pebbles, and seal. Use them in the home corner 'Garden shop'.
• Write stories about 'The very small seed' or 'The surprising seed'.
• Grow some of the seeds.

Questions
How did the children know how to match up the little seeds?
Can they guess what the plants or flowers will be like?
Can they guess whereabouts on a plant the seeds usually grow?

AT1, AT2 (i/ii)

Growth

Objectives
To observe seeds and growth.

What you need
A variety of seeds and some plants eg hyacinth or amaryllis, pots, soil, empty plastic sweet jars, black sugar paper.

What to do
Set up a growth area in the classroom with several varieties of plant. A combination of fast-growing plants such as amaryllis, cress or mung beans will keep the interest of the children.

Put a few small holes near the base of a plastic jar and fill with soil. Push pea or green bean seeds into the soil around the sides so that they show. Make a black paper collar for the jar. What do the children think will happen? When? Water sparingly but regularly.

Follow-up
• Chart the growth of the fast-growing seeds or plants in the classroom.
• Try measuring some of the bigger seeds dry, then leaving them overnight in water and measuring them again. How many fit into a spoon or a babyfood jar before and after soaking?
• Plant out some of the seedlings in your school garden, with lolly sticks for their names and low fencing if possible. Photograph their growth.

Questions
Are seedlings the same colour as the seeds they come from?
Why do the children think some seeds have grown more quickly than others?
What happened to the seeds in the water?

AT1, AT2 (i/ii/iv)

20

The sound of seeds

Objective
To investigate the sounds we can make with seeds.

What you need
A variety of seeds, yoghurt pots, sticky tape, papier mâché, paint, varnish.

What to do
What sounds do the seeds make if we rattle them in our hands? In a milk bottle? Put a handful of seeds into each yoghurt pot and stick another pot over the top. Cover with papier mâché, paint and varnish.

Do the smallest seeds make the quietest sounds?

What do the sounds remind the children of?

Follow-up
• Use pebbles or counters instead of seeds. Do they sound the same?
• Use the shakers to provide sound effects for a story about seeds, or *Jack and the beanstalk*.
• Record it on audio-tape for them to listen to and join in with again later.
• Compare the seed shakers with commercial percussion shakers; are they the same or different?

Questions
What do the children have to do with their hands to make the seed shakers rattle?
Can they make quiet sounds?
What do they think might be inside other percussion instruments?

AT1, AT3 (i), AT4 (iv) D&M

Growth and sound

Objective

To apply to a 'design and make' activity the knowledge gained by observing plants.

What you need

Junk materials including tins with lids, bottle tops, seeds and pebbles, adhesive or sticky tape, string, kitchen roll tubes, poster tubes or garden canes, a hair drier or electric fan, large coffee tins full of sand (or another stabilising medium), big nails or bolts, cotton thread.

What to do

Look at some plants in the classroom. Smell the leaves, stems and flowers. How can we tell which plant is which? Do a blindfold test with three or four plants.

What if the plants had to attract the insects by sound? Let the children help make tall plants which make an attractive noise, using the junk materials. Use the tubes or canes as stems.

Stick the stems firmly in the tins, and show how the hairdrier or fan can simulate the blowing of the wind.

Follow-up

• Add decoration to the plants with tissue/shiny paper etc.
• Tape record the sound of each plant.
• Compare the plant noises with noises made by percussion instruments.
• Use the plants to make up a story.

Questions

What happens to the loose, swinging parts of the plants when the 'wind' blows?
Which of the objects used make a high sound? Which make a low sound?
What do the sounds remind you of?

AT1, AT3 (i), AT4 (iv) D&M

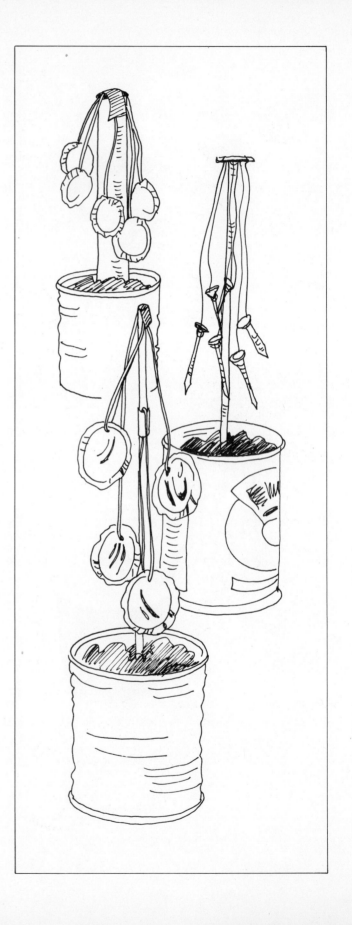

Minibeasts

Objective
To observe the variety of animal life.

What you need
White sheets, insect viewers, empty water tank and other containers, magnifying glasses, microscope if available, spoons. Habitat materials eg fallen twigs and branches, big stones, jars, tree bark or pieces of wood.

What to do
Set up a small habitat area in the school grounds, near a hedge or fence, to encourage small creatures to live there. Put the jars on their sides and raise some of the wood at an angle to provide shade. Leave for a week or more.

Use this area for observing and collecting small animals. Hold the sheet under the branches of a tree, and shake the branches to release other creatures.

Bring some of the minibeasts into the classroom; observe, discuss and draw them. Afterwards, release them.

Follow-up
● Discuss making an indoor habitat for one or more of the minibeasts. What will it need to be like to keep the animals comfortable? Should it be cool or warm, dark or light, dry or moist? What food will they need? How long should we keep them inside? (See 'Animal habitats').

Questions
What do little animals do to avoid being discovered, caught or eaten?
What games do we play which involve hiding or running away?
What do we do when we want to hide or escape?

AT1, AT2 (i/ii/iii) D&M

Animal habitats

Objective
To apply the knowledge gained by observing animals to making a habitat for them.

What you need
Boxes, trays, a water tank, empty plastic sweet jars, other jars, cake tins, soil, newspaper, sand, stones, tin lids, leaves as appropriate, clear acetate, sticky tape.

What to do
Observe the chosen creatures closely.

Use the children's ideas as well as your own to set up a habitat appropriate for the animals, bearing in mind their comfort and needs. Some creatures will need a dark and unexposed area or a black paper cover.

Caterpillars need the appropriate sorts of fresh leaves every day, so make sure that there is room in their jar or container to accommodate enough fresh food.

Always plan on an early release of the animals.

Follow-up
• Observe the animals over the next few days.
• Draw pictures or write about the food and conditions the animals like best.
• Discuss the sorts of animals kept by humans in the home and in zoos.
• Make animal models with junk, dough or Plasticine, and make habitats for them from twigs etc.

Questions
How do the animals move in their new homes? Where do they prefer to be? Can the children see any changes in the creatures or in the habitats?

AT1, AT2 (i/ii/iii) D&M

Fish

Objectives
To observe fish and their characteristics.

What you need
A friendly fishmonger, paper, crayons, newspaper, tray, plaster of Paris, bowl, spoon.

What to do
Arrange a visit to the local fishmonger's (or bring in a variety of fish).

Observe the fish, and notice their similarities and differences. Ask the fishmonger to fillet a plaice and give you the skeleton with the head if possible.

Bring the skeleton back to school, together with a complete (gutted) fish eg herring, and some fish fingers.

Feel the skin. What comes off on your fingers? What shape are the scales? Where are the eyes? What does the fish smell like? Fry, bake or grill the fish and the fish fingers and taste them.

Line the tray with thick newspaper and lie the plaice skeleton inside. Make up the plaster and pour over the skeleton to make a complete and fairly thick cast. Allow to set, feeling the plaster regularly.

Follow-up
• Draw sea and river pictures.
• Make fish for the home corner 'fishmonger's' with paper fish shapes or make a fish mobile to hang from the ceiling.

Questions
How do the children think fish swim? Do all water creatures swim like that? How do humans swim? How many of the children can swim? Can we stay underwater like the fish?

AT1, AT2 (i/ii)

25

Birds

Objectives
To observe birds and explore their behaviour and appearance.

What you need
Bird table with suitable food, or a bag of peanuts or half a coconut to hang up. (This should mostly be done in winter – feeding wild birds is less recommended during the rest of the year.)

As many feathers as you can collect, paint, inks, paper.

What to do
Observe the birds as and when you can. Look at their colours, their beaks, and the way they fly, walk and hop. Do they come alone or in groups? Look at and feel the feathers. Cut open the shaft of a big feather. What do the children notice? What will happen if you dip a hollow feather in ink? Try it.

Can the children draw or write with the feather pens? Can they paint with the feathery ends?

Follow-up
• Use feathers to make collages.
• Try oiling a feather with vegetable oil. Sprinkle with water. What happens?
• Find books about birds.
• Make a display of feathers and things made of feathers.

Questions
What would it be like for us if we had hollow bones, like the birds' feathers? What would it be like for the birds if they had solid feathers? What are water-birds' feathers like?
Can the children find or think of things that are 'as light as a feather'?

AT1, AT2 (ii)

Sand and water

Chapter three

'What is our world made of?' This sort of question prompts many of the investigations which young children undertake.

Sand is a common feature on this earth, and it is unusual in having the properties of a solid (rock particles) and a liquid (it pours and trickles).

Water is usually experienced as a liquid, but it can easily become solid ice.

Looking at the behaviour of these two substances, together with an investigation into air, will give the children first-hand experience of what their world is made up of — solids, liquids and gases.

Looking at sand

Objectives
To investigate sand and its properties.

What you need
A sand tray, water, forks, spoons, sandwheels, funnels, open containers, empty lemonade bottles, small shovels, trowels.

What to do
Put some of the objects into the dry sand for play. Ask the children to discover what they can use the different objects for, and then share their findings with the class.

After a few days change the objects and repeat the process of playing and explaining.

Make the sand wet and let the children play with it again. What happens with the tools and containers now?

Follow-up
• Ask the children to build sandcastles, bridges or caves with dry sand and then with wet sand.
• Pretend you do not know what sand is or how to make a sandcastle. Can the children explain to you without showing you how?
• Take photographs of their sand play and structures, and display them.

Questions
When is it better to have dry sand?
When is it better to have wet sand?
Can they find out what builders use sand for?

AT1, AT3 (i)

28

The feel of sand

Objectives
To investigate sand and its properties.

What you need
Dry sand, sieve, containers, paper, adhesive, spatulas or brushes, empty squeezy bottles.

What to do
Ask the children if they can think of a way of 'writing' with sand. Try out their ideas, including writing in the wet sand with fingers, pouring it slowly out of the squeezy bottle etc.

Is there any way of fixing the sand so that the writing cannot be wiped out?

Make a letter or shape with adhesive on paper. Sprinkle the sand over it and shake off the excess. Can the children write their names like that? Draw a picture?

Follow-up
• With eyes closed, play guessing games with sand initials.
• Invite a sight-disabled person to come and talk with the children. Borrow some Braille script to feel.
• Make sand 'gardens' in trays, with shells, pebbles, twigs, feathers and little mirrors. Photograph them.

Questions
Ask the children what the sand feels like in their fingers.
Can they guess what sand is made of?

AT1, AT3 (i)

The sound of sand

Objectives
To investigate sand and the sound it makes.

What you need
Dry sand, yoghurt pots or plastic margarine containers, sticky tape, empty plastic bottles, tins with lids, acrylics or other things for colouring.

What to do
Let the children trickle sand through their fingers into a tray. Can they hear anything? Do it again.

What if the sand trickles into a pot or tin? Rattle the container gently.

Let them choose a yoghurt pot or tin to put sand in, and seal it. What sound does it make now?

Follow-up
• Decorate the sand shakers.
• Sort the shakers into sets, using the children's criteria as well as your own.
• Use the shakers to illustrate a familiar poem or song.
• Tape record it.

Questions
What is the sand doing inside the container to make a noise?
What else can they find that makes a noise when you rattle it?

AT1, AT3 (i), AT4 (iv)

Sand-timers

Objective
To observe the properties of sand by making and using sand-timers.

What you need
One-, three- and five-minute sand-timers, jam jars, clear drinking cups, empty squeezy bottles, dry sand, a craft knife or scissors, sticky tape.

What to do
Give the sand-timers to the children to look at. Use them to time activities eg can they go to the door and back again before the sand in the one-minute timer runs through? Can they go and get a drink of water? Can they wash their hands and dry them before the three-minute sand-timer runs out of sand?

Take the plastic nozzles off the squeezy bottles, then cut the tops off the bottles five or six centimetres down. Put different amounts of dry sand into the drinking cups. Tape the bottle-tops on to the cups, or push in firmly. Invert each over a jam jar to make your own sand-timers.

Follow-up
• Use the timers in PE activities and games.
• Put the water-wheel into the sand tray, together with funnels and containers; let the children experiment.
• Discuss clocks and time-keeping. Older children can make cardboard clocks with hands mounted in the centre with paper-fasteners.

Questions
What kinds of clock do the children have at home? Do any of them have egg-timers?

AT1, AT3 (i), AT4 D&M

31

Looking at water

Objectives
To investigate water and its properties.

What you need
Tank with water toys and equipment eg watermill, pump, squeezy bottles, siphon tubing, eye-droppers, syringes, funnels, jam jars and spoons.

What to do
Introduce one new item of equipment into the water play every two or three days, and take out another. Can the children tell you later how each object works?

Can they explain to someone who has never seen water before what it is like? Tape record their explanations.

Fill jam jars with water, and let the children feel the water with their fingers. What do their hands look like in the water? Through the glass? Behind the jar? What does the spoon look like in the water?

Follow-up
• Put mirrors, lenses and old spectacles on a table for the children to look at. Add a few objects to view with the lenses.
• Look at the taps, flush-toilets and water fountains to see how they work.

Questions
Can the children guess where our water comes from? What would it be like if we had no water in the taps?

AT1, AT3 (i), AT4 (iii/iv)

Floating

Objective
To investigate floating.

What you need
Water tank, a selection of floating and non-floating objects eg ball, cork, pencil, spoon, tin, paper-clips, conkers, pebbles, empty lemonade bottles, arm bands.

What to do
Show the children the arm bands. Do any of them use these? When and why do we need them?

Can they guess which things will float in the water and which ones might sink? Sort the objects into sets, and then try them. Were the children surprised at the results?

Can they find other objects in the classroom that will float or that will sink?

Follow-up
• Can the children make the plastic bottle float? Can they make it sink, or float just under the water?
• Photograph or draw the sets of floaters and non-floaters.
• Make a chart of the children's water experience, perhaps divided into paddlers, beginners and swimmers.
• Can the children use the junk materials to make a boat?

Questions
Do they notice anything special about the things that float?
What happens when the water is salty?

AT1, AT3 (i), AT4 (iii)

Ice and water

Objectives
To investigate water and its different states.

What you need
Access to a freezer compartment, water tank, water, balloons.

What to do
Two or more days before they are needed, fill two balloons with water, fasten and freeze them. The skin may break in the process, but that will not matter. When these are ready, fill another two balloons with water.

Show the ice balloons and water balloons to the children.

What do they feel like? What happens if you press them, or drop them near the table? What will happen if you put them in water? Remove the balloons from around the ice, and watch what happens to the ice when you put it in water.

Follow-up
● Blow up two balloons and compare them with the balloons full of ice and water.

● Freeze water in other flexible and non-flexible containers eg rubber gloves, freezer bags with elastic bands tied randomly round them, ice-ball bags, ice-cube trays. What shapes does the ice take?

Questions
Where do the ice objects melt first? How long do they take to melt?

AT1, AT3 (i/iii), AT4 (ii/iii)

balloon full of air

balloon full of ice

balloon full of water

Water paintings

Objectives
To investigate water and evaporation.

What you need
Bowls or buckets, water, brushes, paper, and a dry, sunny day.

What to do
Show the children the clear water. Is it possible to make a picture with just water? Take them outside to 'paint' something with the water on the playground. Let them do pictures and patterns. How long do they think their paintings will last?

Follow-up
• Do some plain water paintings on paper. Hang them out to dry and time how long they stay wet.
• Make up water paints with colour and do drip paintings, spatter paintings with combs and nailbrushes, fold-paintings, blow-paintings with straws, string-paintings, finger-paintings etc.

Questions
Where do they think the water goes when a water painting dries out?
Will it come back again?
How long does it take for their paintings to dry?
How long does it take a puddle to dry after it rains?

AT1, AT3 (i/iii)

Bridges over the water

Objectives
To look at ways of crossing water and investigate bridges.

What you need
Blue crêpe paper, commercial construction kits, junk materials, adhesive, newspaper and sticky tape.

What to do
Make a long 'river' of blue crêpe paper approximately 20 cm wide, stuck down across the classroom floor.

Ask the children what they can put there, or make, to cross the river. Stepping stones? Bridges?

Let the children use bricks, construction kits, junk materials and anything else they can think of to make bridges.

Older children could try to make a free-standing bridge using just newspaper and sticky tape.

Follow-up
● Measure the bridges – their height and span.
● Are the bridges strong enough to support a toy car on top?
● Visit a nearby bridge, and look at its construction.

Questions
Can the children guess how people might cross rivers where there are no bridges?
What are real bridges made of?
What was the hardest part of making their bridges?

AT1, AT3 (i), AT4 (iii) D&M

Air and flight

Chapter four

Air – that intangible, invisible substance that surrounds us and on which we all depend – can be a difficult thing for children to comprehend.

Investigating its existence and how it behaves will help to establish its importance in the children's minds.

Playing with air in the form of balloons, wind-balls and bubbles, and 'controlling' the forces of air pressure and gravity in making kites, planes and parachutes will encourage understanding of this fascinating substance and the role it plays in our lives.

Air is real

Objectives

To show that air is real by making it visible and showing that it exerts pressure.

What you need

A transparent water tank, water, baby-food jars or clear plastic pots, clear food-wrapping film, elastic bands, a skewer, siphon tubing, eye-droppers, syringes, thin paints and paper.

What to do

Show the children the 'empty' jars. Ask if they can see anything inside. Tie some clear film over the jars with elastic bands, and let the children try pushing the jars down to the bottom of the tank. What can they feel?

Hold one of the jars down and pierce the film. What has to come out before the water can get in?

Ask the children to try different ways of carrying water in the eye-droppers and syringes. How can they get the air out in order to let the water in?

Follow-up

• Make a submarine with a squeezy bottle; fill it up with water in the tank, then blow air into it using the siphon tubing. What will happen?
• Use the eye-droppers and syringes to carry paint on to pieces of paper for blow-paintings and fold-paintings.

Questions

How much push did the children have to use to keep the covered jars under water? What was pushing them back? How much 'blow' did they have to use to do blow-paintings?

AT1, AT3 (i), AT4 (iii)

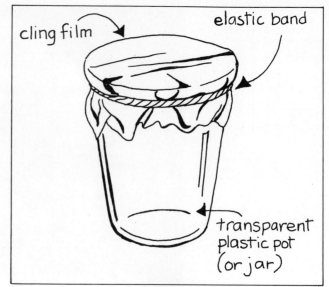

cling film

elastic band

transparent plastic pot (or jar)

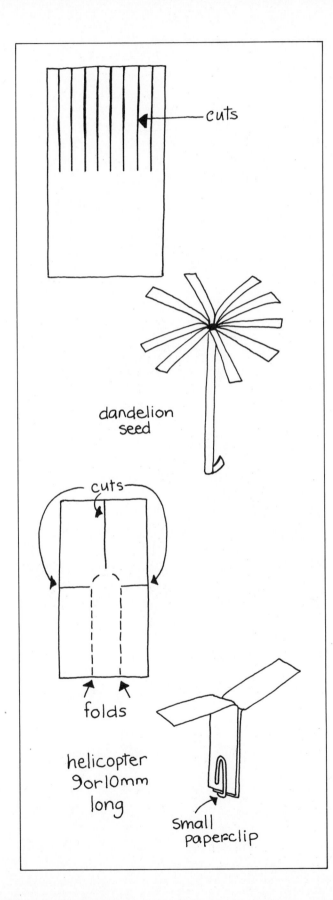

cuts

dandelion
seed

cuts

folds

helicopter
9 or 10mm
long

small
paperclip

Air travel – dandelion see...

w

Objectives
To show how air can hold th...
make them move or travel.

What you need
Paper, light-weight scissors.

What to do
Let the children make paper 'dandelion seeds'. Give them pieces of thin paper, about 4cm by 7cm. Help them (if necessary) to make a row of cuts along one side of the paper, cutting in as far as the centre. Fold the paper up tightly, bend the strips of paper so that they stand out from the centre and turn up at the uncut end.

What will happen if you let the dandelion seeds drop? Try it. What happens if you try it outside, especially if there is wind?

Follow-up
• Measure in footsteps or strides the distance travelled by the dandelion seeds.
• Try making dandelion seeds with other pieces of thin paper.
• Look at some real dandelion seeds, draw them and see what happens when you drop them.
• Look at helicopters in books.

Questions
What will happen if the dandelion seeds are dropped upside-down? Why do the children think that happens?

AT1, AT4 (iii) D&M

nd strength

Objectives
To show that moving air has strength and direction by observing and measuring the wind.

What you need
Short sticks, garden canes or paint brushes, crêpe paper, sticky tape, Plasticine, a long thin scarf or tights.

What to do
Cut thin strips of crêpe paper and attach three or four to the end of each stick. Stand outside and watch the effect of the wind on the paper. (Do not expect too much accuracy as the wind often gusts and changes direction.)

One stick can be embedded in Plasticine in a tin and left outside for further observation.

A 'wind sock' can be made with the scarf or tights.

Follow-up
● Let the children help you make a large chart for measuring the wind's strength and use it for a class weather record.
● Read the story of the argument between the sun and the wind (Aesop's Fables). Dramatise it with movement and percussion.

Questions
What sort of things does the wind move? What would it be like if we never had any moving air?

AT1, AT3 (iv) D&M

Windfalls

Objectives
To experience air pressure and the force of gravity by trapping air in a parachute.

What you need
Pieces of polythene about 30cm square (eg from opened plastic bags), paper, equal lengths of string, toy farm animals.

What to do
Remind the children of the rhyme 'Hey, diddle, diddle'. Drop the toy cow and ask if they can suggest how to stop the cow from hurting herself when she falls down from the moon.

Try out their suggestions, reminding them (if necessary) of the idea of a parachute.

Fasten one end of each of four pieces of string to the corners of the polythene. Tie the other ends to the cow, and drop her from different heights.

Try the same thing with the other animals, using bigger pieces of polythene and longer lengths of string. Experiment with dropping them outside.

Follow-up
● Make up stories or pictures about 'The jumping cow's adventures'.
● In PE do jumping games and activities.

Questions
What is getting under the parachute to hold it up? What do the children think is pulling things down towards the ground? (Accept their explanations – introduce the idea of the pull of gravity only if you think it is appropriate.)

AT1, AT4 (iii) D&M

Air pressure — balloons

Objective
To experience the force of air pressure.

What you need
Several balloons, food colourings, straws or eye-droppers, kitchen or sugar paper, pin, tissues.

What to do
Blow up a balloon. Ask the children what will happen if the balloon bursts, then pop it. Ask the children what would happen if there was something inside the balloon.

Introduce a little colouring (about a teaspoonful) into the balloon using the straw or eye-dropper. Wrap the paper loosely but completely round the balloon. Let a child pop it.

Try again with different colourings on the same or different papers.

Follow-up
• Use dye crystals or food colourings on old white sheeting to make fabric patterns and use as a display.
• Use black ink on grey paper to make rainy-day pictures.

Questions
Can the children explain what is happening to the skin of the balloon? What is happening to the air inside the balloon?

AT1, AT3 (i), AT4 (iii/iv)

Giant bubbles

Objectives
To look at the shape, colours and reflections in bubbles.

What you need
Florist's wire, empty squeezy bottles, cut as shown, small jars or pots, bubble solution (one tablespoon of washing-up liquid to half a pint of water), shallow dish or bowl.

What to do
Bend the ends of the florist's wire into loops. Working in small groups, let each child make her own bubbles from a thin film of bubble solution.

Are the bubbles the same shape? Can they blow a bubble that is *not* round? Try making wire triangles and squares.

Cut the squeezy bottles in half. Make cuts to fan out the ends. Take off the nozzles and clean the opening thoroughly.

Give the children the squeezy bottle blowers to blow giant bubbles. What can they see on the surface of the bubbles?

Follow-up
• Let the children paint pictures of what they see on the giant bubbles.
• Can they write a story or draw a picture about what it might be like to live in a rainbow country?
• Let the children look at reflections in mirrors and lenses.

Questions
Are all the reflections in the bubbles the same way up? Are they the right way up? Can the children explain this?

AT1, AT3 (i), AT4 (iii/iv)

Kites

Objectives
To experience air lift and to look at aspects of flight.

What you need
Tissue-paper cut into small kites and streamers, art straws or spills, adhesive or sticky tape, cotton thread, paper-clips.

What to do
This activity is suitable for older children. Stick straws or spills on to the kites as support struts, allowing space to attach a paper-clip near or over the cross-piece. Fasten long pieces of thread to the clips. Let the children try out these kites in several ways — without a tail, with a short tail, with a long tail and with several tails. What do they notice? What happens when streamers are attached to the other corners?

Follow-up
- Try the tissue-paper kites outside (choose a fairly calm day).
- Try making bigger tissue kites.
- Bring in a full-sized kite to investigate.

Questions
What difference do the tails make to the kite's flight?
Why do the children think this happens?

AT1, AT4 (iii) D&M

Painting and colour

Chapter five

The world is full of wonderful colour – the result of objects absorbing or reflecting light from the spectrum.

Our eyes and emotions are responsive to certain colours, and much of our adult lives are spent determining the colours we will wear, live with, or react to on the road.

Developing a familiarity with colour is one of the first experiences we need to give our children. Finding colours around them and making and choosing colours are good activities for children in the early years, and looking at the effects of light is an enjoyable way to extend their understanding.

Dissolving and mixing powder paints

Objectives
To look at colours and experience the way paints float, sink, mix and dissolve.

What you need
Jam jars, powder paints, spoons, paper, water.

What to do
Fill the jars three-quarters full of water. Give each child a supply of powder paint and a spoon. Can they guess what will happen if they drop a spoonful of paint on to the water? Try, without stirring. What does it look like from the top? From the side? Let them try with other colours. (Powder paints of different colours usually dissolve at different rates.) What happens when they try two different colours in the same jar?

Ask the children what will happen if you mix dry powder paint. Put spoonfuls of dry paint powder on to the paper. What colours do they get?

Try the same activity with wet paint. What colours do the children get this time?

Follow-up
• Do finger-painting on different surfaces.
• Mix different coloured powder paints.
• Let the children take turns pouring into the sink the paints they have mixed with water. What happens as the coloured waters mix?

Questions
Do the powders which sink when sprinkled on to water feel any different from the ones which float? Is there any difference between them in warm water?

AT1, AT3 (i), AT4 (iv)

Painting tools

Objectives
To experience mixing colours and the use of tools.

What you need
Prepared paints (some thickened with paste), spoons, brushes, spatulas, smooth table surfaces, paper.

What to do
Use the thick paint. Can the children guess how much paint they can carry on one finger? Find out which tool will carry the most.

Use the paints for finger-painting and prints. How far does the paint spread out? Put paint on to paper for folding into symmetrical pictures.

Follow-up
● Try the same activities using thin paint. Does it make any difference?
● Try the paints out on different papers and cloths. What happens to the paint?
● Make painted cloths into small wall hangings — reinforce the tops with sticks, and suspend them with string.

Questions
Which was the best tool for carrying paint?
Can the children think of anything even better?
What was it like trying to carry the thin paint?
When you make a print, does it come out the right way round?

AT1, AT3 (i)

Beautiful black

Objective
To consider the absence of colour by using greys and blacks.

What you need
Black pencils, both soft and hard, charcoal, black crayons.

What to do
Give the children the pencils. What 'colour' do the pencils give? Can the children make *really* black patches? Let them try. Compare with the crayons and charcoal. Which ones are shiny? Do the shiny ones look the blackest? Can they use the pencils etc to make a rainy-day picture? A night-time picture?

Follow-up
• Ask the children to guess what is inside a pencil. Score one with a craft knife or similar tool and cut it open along its length to show the graphite inside. What does it feel like?
• Show the children some barbecue charcoal to feel and draw with.
• Can they think of natural things that are black? If possible, bring some black things in to look at and investigate.
• Set up a 'black is beautiful' table.

Questions
If all the coloured paints are mixed up, what colour will they make?
If you overlap pieces of coloured acetate film, what colour is made?
Ask the children what their favourite colour is. How do they feel when they wear that colour?

AT1, AT3 (i), AT4 (iv)

Camouflage

Objectives
To apply the children's experience of colour to looking at camouflage and contrast.

What you need
Prepared paints, brushes, cut-out white paper butterflies, (about 30cm across), cut-out caterpillars (about 15cm long), bricks, big stones, leaves, twigs.

What to do
Ask the children how to help to hide the white paper creatures from the things which might eat them (eg hungry birds). Try their ideas out using the caterpillars and the leaves and stones. Can the children use the paints to give the creatures patterns and colours on their backs to make them invisible?

The creatures want their friends and families to be able to find them. Can the children paint the underneath sides to make them noticeable?

Follow-up
● Look at pictures of creatures, small and large, in books and in their natural habitat. Which ones are camouflaged?
● Paint backdrops of the sea, the woods and the mountains. Let the children paint animals to 'hide' or 'show up' in the pictures.

Questions
How could the children camouflage themselves?
If an animal is very brightly coloured, how will it look after or defend itself?

AT1, AT2 (ii), AT3 (i) D&M

Colour in the environment

Objective
To look at colour in the natural environment.

What you need
Access to the school garden, a hedge, wooded area or park, painted strips of colour.

What to do
Let the children take the painted strips of colour outside. Can they find objects which match the colours? Which colours do they find the most? Which do they find the least?

For older children have ready some varied greens eg pale yellowish green, dark bluish green etc. Can they match these up outside?

Follow-up
• Make a collection of objects to classify in the classroom by colours. Older children could identify subsets in the green set etc.
• The children could draw around the objects and colour them in.

Questions
Can the children find out what makes the growing things green?
Try sticking a paper strip over a growing leaf and watch the effect over a week or two.
Which colours do they see most in the street?

AT1, AT2 (ii/iv), AT4 (iv)

Dyeing

Objective
To observe the change in colour made by dyeing cloth.

What you need
White cotton or half-cotton sheeting, cold water dyes, fixative, salt, buckets or bowls, kettle, jug, large paint brushes (reversed for stirring), water, elastic bands, string, beads or seeds, rubber gloves, pegs.

What to do
Tear the sheeting into individual squares for each child, plus some spares.

Give the children the beads, seeds or pebbles and some elastic bands, and show them how to fasten the seeds in by wrapping the bands round.

Make up the dyes (use dark, strong colours only). Ask what will happen to the cloth in the dye. What will happen to the cloth underneath the bands?

Immerse the cloths in the containers of dye and stir gently. When ready, hang the cloths out to dry. When dry, undo the elastic bands and look at the patterns.

Follow-up
• Use the cloths for headscarfs and kerchiefs in a folk dance, or to make colourful movement patterns.
• Try dyeing cloth with vegetable dyes.
• Over-dye with two or more colours, removing some bands each time.

Questions
What stopped the colour getting into all the cloth? Can the children think of anything they could use to stop the colour getting into the cloth? (Try batik with wax.)

AT1, AT3 (i) D&M

Coloured liquids

Objective
To observe the effect of colour on liquids.

What you need
Strong inks or food colourings, jars of water, straws.

What to do
Remind the children or help them to discover how to carry water in a straw, with a finger over the top.

Ask them what they might see if they let a drop of ink fall into a jar of water without stirring. What will the ink do? Where will it go? Try another drop. Try a different colour in fresh water.

Follow-up
• Draw pictures of the inks in the water.
• Make a poem using the words the children suggest about the movement of the ink.
• Use the ideas for movement in PE.

Questions
What will happen to the ink if we stir it? What will happen if we leave the inky water to stand overnight? What happens if we slowly add orange or black currant squash to water?

AT1, AT3 (i), AT4 (iv)

Marbling

Objectives
To observe the effect of oil on water, and look at oil paints or marbling inks.

What you need
Two watertight trays (a pale colour, if possible), vegetable oil, spoons, oil paints in solution with white spirit, or marbling inks, paint brushes, reversed for stirring, good quality paper.

What to do
Ask the children what they think will happen if you put a drop of oil on to the water in the tray. Try it.

Lay a piece of paper on the surface of the water and lift it off. What happens? Hold the paper up to the light. What do you notice?

Use artist's white spirit to a depth of 1cm in babyfood jars to dissolve 1cm-long squeezes of oil paint (primary colours). Make sure that only the teacher uses the white spirit.

Show the children the jars of oil paint dissolved in white spirit. Can they guess what these paints will do in the water? Put spoonfuls of each colour on to the water (most is needed at the start of the marbling). Watch. Let a child stir gently before taking a print or two, then repeat.

Follow-up
• Use the marbled paper for drawing on with crayons, as backgrounds for black silhouettes, for covering books, or for making greetings cards.

Questions
How many colours were there at the start of the marbling? How many are there now? Are there patches with no colour?

AT1, AT3 (i), AT4 (iv)

Colour and light

Objective
To look at the effects of coloured light filters.

What you need
Pieces of black sugar paper, pieces of coloured acetate film, transparent wrappers from chocolates, sticky tape, adhesive.

What to do
Fold the sugar paper and help the children to cut shapes from it, leaving holes of different shapes in the paper. Stick the coloured acetate film over the holes, either in single or double thickness. Reinforce the edges with sticky tape. Ask what the coloured film will do to the light coming in through the window. Stick the sheets of paper with acetate film patches over the window with masking tape. Are the children right in their expectations?

Follow-up
• Cut out silhouettes of objects or people and cover the spaces with coloured acetate film.
• Try overlapping several colours or layers over a cut-out shape.
• If any houses or churches nearby have stained-glass windows try to arrange to let the children see them.
• Make little houses from boxes, with chocolate wrappers on the windows.

Questions
What is it like looking out of the window through the colours?
What about looking inside from the playground?
Why do people choose to have stained glass in their houses or churches?

AT1, AT4 (iv)

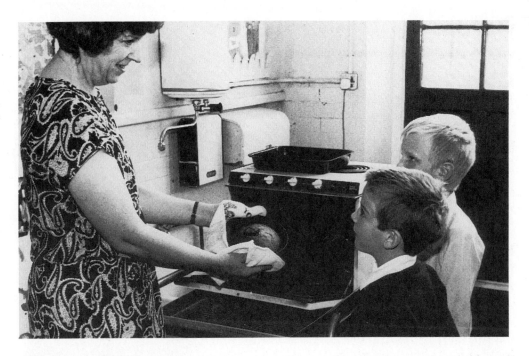

Cooking

Chapter six

Investigating food is one of the best activities we can use to encourage scientific skills and understanding. There is great scope for observation using all the senses; looking, smelling, feeling, tasting and even listening. There are many changes we can observe in food preparation; dissolving, freezing and heating.

Mathematics and language are part of the process; the children are given experience of the familiar and the unfamiliar, with special opportunities for children from different backgrounds to talk about and identify foods and flavours.

Skills of prediction can be encouraged, with chances to discover by actually doing things.

There is a chance to teach children about hygiene, as well as co-operation with each other, and they will all share the pleasure of eating the results. The ideas in this chapter are best undertaken with small groups.

Potatoes

Objective
To look at the differences between raw and cooked potatoes.

What you need
Potatoes, access to an oven, skewers, cutlery, plates, butter or margarine.

What to do
Ask the children to bring a large potato each. Provide some spares as well. Wash them. Look at and compare the size, shape, colour and weight of the potatoes.

Cut a spare one in half. Push the skewer or fork into it and listen to the sound; let the children feel the amount of 'push' needed. Prick the skins of all the potatoes with forks and bake them in the oven at gas mark 6, 200°C, 400°F, for one hour or until they are soft when pressed.

Test them again with the skewer and listen. Cut the potatoes in half, let them cool and eat with butter or margarine.

Follow-up
• Use some halved potatoes for printing, with patterns cut out of the flesh.
• Draw pictures of the different ways of serving potatoes; chips, mashed, crisps, roast etc.

Questions
How did the potato skin change when it was cooked?
Was the colour of the potato the same before and after cooking?
Was it the same shape?

AT1, AT3 (i/iii), AT4 (ii)

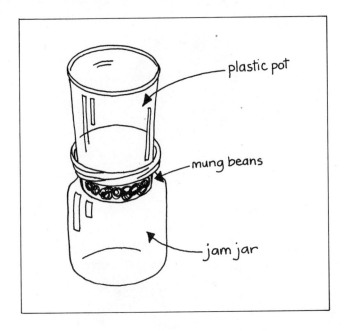

plastic pot

mung beans

jam jar

Beansprouts

Objectives
To investigate and grow mung beans.

What you need
For growing: mung beans, a sprouter — commercial or DIY (see below), oil.

For the stir-fry: vegetables eg mushrooms, onions, white cabbage, Chinese cabbage; stock cube, soy sauce, rice if desired; cooking utensils.

What to do
Make sprouters from transparent drinking cups or yoghurt pots with holes in the bottom, suspended over jam jars. Put in some mung beans and wash with water every day until they sprout. How many days will they take? What do they taste like when they have sprouted?

Use the mung beans in a stir-fry. Slice all the other vegetables thinly and fry together with the mung beans in a little oil for three to four minutes. Add a little water, stock cube and a little soy sauce to taste and cook for a few more minutes.

Follow-up
• Let some mung beans go on sprouting and watch their growth. When the sprouting beans are taller, put on the jam jar lid with a small weight on top and see what happens.
• Use a large mushroom to make a spore print by leaving it undisturbed over a piece of white paper for a day or two.
• In PE think of movements associated with growth.

Questions
What grew first — the roots of the beansprouts or the stalks?
What helped the beans to grow?

AT1, AT2 (i/ii)

Fruit salad

Objective
To observe the colours in fruit.

What you need
A variety of fruits eg red and green apples, orange, banana, and some less familiar fruits, whatever is available; paints, paper and brushes, knife, bowls, spoons.

What to do
Look at and discuss the colours of the fruit skins. Can the children guess what they look like on the inside?

Ask the children to paint a picture of the insides, showing the flesh and seeds, before cutting the fruit open. Then open them and look inside. Paint a picture of what they really look like inside.

Guess what the taste will be like, and then taste the fruit. Cut them up into small pieces for a fruit salad.

Follow-up
• Bring more fruits in and cut them lengthwise and breadthwise. Do they look any different?
• Draw large fruit outlines and make a collage to represent the inside of the fruit.
• Ask the children to draw pictures of how they think the fruit grows.

Questions
How did the insides of the fruit differ from what the children expected?
Does the outside colour give us any clues about the inside colour?
How many shapes did the children see?

AT1, AT2 (ii) D&M

Fruit crumble

Objective
To observe the effects of heating food.

What you need
Fruit eg cooking apples, rhubarb, blackberries or gooseberries; 8 tablespoons of self-raising flour, a pinch of salt, 4 tablespoons of sugar to each kilogram of fruit, and 4 tablespoons of sugar for the crumble topping; 100g margarine; cooking utensils, cooker.

What to do
Ask the children to look at the fruit, squeeze it, smell it, taste it and describe it. What will it look like when it is cooked?

Cut the fruit into small pieces, put it in the base of the oven dish or dishes, sprinkle with sugar and a little water.

Let the children help make up the crumble topping. What does the flour feel like in their fingers? What does the margarine feel like? What will happen to the crumble in the oven?

Cook for 30-40 minutes at gas mark 4, 180°C, 350°F. Cool the crumble and eat it.

Follow-up
• Make pastry with the flour and margarine, and roll out for jam tarts.
• Make charts of favourite fruits and puddings.
• Invite a parent in to make an unfamiliar dish with the children.

Questions
Can the children suggest reasons why we cook so much of our food?
Which foods do they like best raw and which cooked?

AT1, AT2 (i), AT3 (iii), AT4 (ii)

Spices and herbs

Objective
To investigate spices and herbs.

What you need
A variety of spices and herbs (not more than six at a time); jam jars, water, spoons, saucers, magnifying glasses, microscope if available.

What to do
Work in small groups for this activity.

Put a little of each spice into a saucer. What do they look like? Is there any smell? Are any the same to look at? What do they feel like? Touch them and see.

Sprinkle some on to the surface of the water in the jam jars, look and smell again. Try it again in warm water.

What kinds of food do the children think the spices could be used for?

Follow-up
• Bring other spices or herbs to look at.
• Use the spices and herbs in a collage picture or pattern.
• Bring in vegetables to make a vegetable goulash or curry.

Questions
Do any of the children's families use spices or herbs at home?
Can they guess where they might be grown?

AT1, AT2 (i), AT3 (i)

Porridge oats

Objective
To investigate the changes that take place during cooking.

What you need
Porridge oats, saucepan, spoons, bowls, sugar, syrup, milk, salt, wooden spoon.

What to do
Read *The Magic Porridge Pot* or *The Three Bears* before starting to make the porridge. Let the children feel and taste the oatmeal. What does it look like now? What will it look like after cooking?

Follow the instructions on the packet; cook the porridge, put it into the bowls and allow it to cool.

Has it changed? Is anything the same?

Let the children choose a topping — sugar, syrup, milk — then taste it. (Some children may reject it.)

Follow-up
● Make a muesli with the oats, dried fruits and nuts and brown sugar; and try this with milk.
● Turn out the cold porridge. What does it look like underneath?
● Make a collection of cereal packets to illustrate the varieties. Investigate and taste them.
● Find suitable songs, like 'Oats and beans and barley grow'.
● Make a big mural to illustrate the porridge story.

Questions
What happened to the sugar crystals on top of the warm porridge?
What happened to the syrup?
Can anyone guess why so many people have cereal for breakfast?

AT1, AT2 (i), AT3 (i/iii), AT4 (ii) D&M

Jellies

Objective
To investigate dissolving by making jellies.

What you need
Bowls, spoons, kettle, scissors, different jellies, moulds, access to a refrigerator.

What to do
Make sure the children wash their hands first. Look at and feel the jellies – their colour, texture and smell. Count the cubes.

Tear or cut the jellies into little pieces, add cold water and stir. Does anything happen? Add some hot water – is there any change?

Make up the remaining jelly with hot water to ensure it is dissolved completely. Leave the jellies to set and turn them out. Can the children recognise the flavour with their eyes closed?

Follow-up
• Try 'blind' tastings with jelly babies, jelly beans, chocolate buttons and crisps.
• Do more dissolving with other substances.
• In PE do movements like wobbly jellies.

Questions
How did we make the jellies change? What shape were the jellies to start with? What shape were they at the end?

Can the children think of anything else that dissolves in hot water?

AT1, AT3 (i/iii), AT4 (ii)

Food colourings

Objective
To observe the effects of food colourings.

What you need
Cooking utensils, ingredients to make fairy cakes: for 18 cakes — 4 tablespoons of self-raising flour, 4 tablespoons of sugar, 100g margarine, 2 eggs, a little salt; food colourings; icing sugar, toothpicks, cake cases, oven.

What to do
Make up some cake mix (blend the margarine and sugar, add flour, salt and beaten eggs) and divide the mixture into small bowls. What will happen to the mixture if drops of colour are added? Try it. Stir gently.

What will happen during the cooking? Cook the cakes and see. (Gas mark 5, 190°C, 375°F, for 15 to 20 minutes.)

Make up some icing and ice the cakes. Let the children colour and pattern the tops using toothpicks dipped into the food colourings.

Follow-up
● Try a 'blindfold' test — can the children guess which are the blue, green or pink cakes by the taste? Try the same test out on any available and willing adults.
● Paint hard-boiled eggs with the food colourings. Leave them until the following day. What will the eggs be like inside?

Questions
Has the food colouring changed the flavour? Which colour cakes do the children like the best?
What other colours can food have? What colours are curry? Squash? Ice-cream? Sweets?

AT1, AT3 (i/iii), AT4 (ii) D&M

Ice lollies

Objective
To observe the effects of cooling on liquids.

What you need
Ice lollies or 'ice-pops' for each child, and some spares; ice lolly moulds, squash, water, lolly sticks, junk materials and fabrics, access to a freezer or ice-making compartment.

What to do
Show the children one of the 'ice-pops'. Can they think of ways of keeping these frozen until playtime? What if they cannot use the freezer?

Let them use the fabrics and junk materials to wrap up the lollies and leave them. Later, unwrap them and see which ones are still frozen.

Prepare some ice lollies with the squash and water and leave them to freeze. Observe and eat them before the end of the day.

Follow-up
• Ask the children how to keep a baked potato or a cup of tea warm.
• Freeze some ice in other containers. Look at the shape of the ice, and feel it.

Questions
What materials seemed to be best for keeping the 'ice-pops' cold?
Which food do we like best ice-cold, and which do we like hot?

AT1, AT3 (i/iii), AT4 (ii)

Pancakes

Objective
To investigate the changes caused by heat.

What you need
A large bowl, frying-pan, spoons, self-raising flour, salt, eggs, oil, milk, water, sugar, butter or margarine, lemon juice, cooker, plates, forks, knives, toy frying-pans and Plasticine.

What to do
Make up some pancake batter with 6 tablespoons of flour, 250ml of water and milk, a pinch of salt and one egg. Beat the batter with a spoon until creamy and smooth. (Makes eight pancakes.)

Heat one teaspoon of oil in the pan (but be careful to take safety precautions). What do the children think will happen to the batter in the hot pan? Put in two or three tablespoons and pour thinly over the pan. What happens? Toss or turn the pancake over, cook it on the other side and put it on a plate.

Spread the pancake with butter, sprinkle it with sugar or lemon juice, cut and eat it.

Follow-up
• Read about and make pictures of *The Runaway Pancake*.
• Make Plasticine pancakes in the home corner and let the children toss these in their frying-pans.

Questions
What was the batter like before heating? After heating?
Can the children think of any other foods that are shaped like a circle?

AT1, AT3 (i/iii), AT4 (ii)

Chocolate fudge

Objective
To investigate food textures.

What you need
125g margarine, 4 tablespoons of sugar, 6 tablespoons of dried milk powder, 4 tablespoons of fresh milk, 4 tablespoons of raisins, 2 tablespoons of drinking chocolate, 200g crushed rich tea biscuits for each 7 inch cake tin.

What to do
Let the children have a taste of each of the ingredients and say how they feel on their tongues. Which do they like best?

Make the fudge as follows. Crush the biscuits. Melt the margarine and sugar together, add the fresh milk and the dried milk and mix well.

Add the raisins and the drinking chocolate, then stir in the biscuit crumbs. Press the mixture into the cake tin, cool and cut into cubes.

What is the texture like now? Which ingredients can they still taste?

Follow-up
• Bring in a few different varieties of fudge for a guessing and tasting game.
• Make a collection of the packets of their favourite sweets, and sort them into sets.
• Make the fudge to sell at school functions.

Questions
With which part of the tongue could the children taste things?
Can they guess what the raisins are made from? Or where they grow?

AT1, AT3 (i/iii)

Lighting up

Chapter seven

Work on electricity and magnetism needs to be included in early learning to develop familiarity with something which dominates our modern technology.

For young children a good straightforward kit is essential (eg the *Middlesex Poly Electricity 5-13* kit). This would contain battery holders, bulbs and bulb holders, simple connecting wires, switches, buzzers, motors and crocodile clips. A good kit is one which is easy to use and gives clues for completing circuits, etc, by the design of its connections.

Where 'electricity kit' is mentioned, it is assumed that one or two such kits, or their component parts, are available, together with appropriate 1.5v batteries.

Strong magnets are essential if children are to feel the force of magnetism. Buy or borrow bar, horseshoe, disc and cylinder magnets and magnetic strips for extension work.

Circuits

Objective
To give experience of electricity in a circuit.

What you need
An electricity kit.

What to do
Ask the children to use the equipment to make one of the bulbs light up.

When they succeed ask them to try to make two bulbs light up . . . then three.

What happens if each bulb has its own 'circle' connected to the battery? Can they feel anything else when they touch the bulb? NB Emphasise *never* to touch mains electrical points.

Follow-up
• Give the children the buzzers and motors without telling them what they are. Can they make them work and tell you what they are? (They may need guidance on which way round to try out the buzzer if they do not succeed.)
• Can they make a model of the circuit with the lights, using junk materials stuck on to card?

Questions
Can the children guess what is making the bulbs light up? What do they think is inside the batteries? (Accept their explanations.)

What else did the electricity do besides making the bulbs light up?

How can they make the light bulbs go out?

AT1, AT4 (i/iii)

batteries in battery holder

bulb in bulb holder

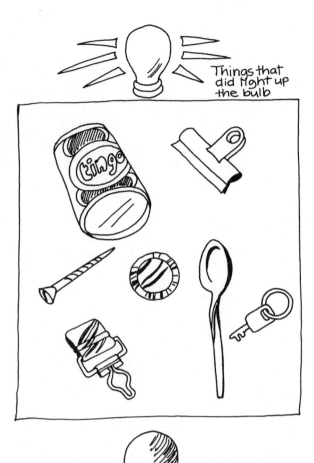

Things that did light up the bulb

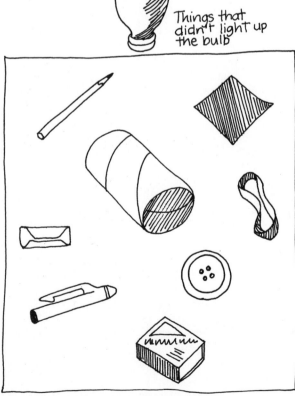

Things that didn't light up the bulb

Conducting materials

Objective
To give experience of electrical circuits and materials that will conduct electricity.

What you need
Electricity kit, various objects, such as metal and plastic spoons, pencils, cloth, paper, foil, coins, tin cans, keys, cork, polystyrene tray etc.

What to do
Ask the children to make the bulb light up again. Disconnect the circuit and add an extra connecting wire to create a gap between the two wires.

Can the children make the bulb light up now (by making the two wire end-clips touch)? Do the children think electricity can travel through anything else to make the bulb light up?

Join the gap in the circuit with one of the objects that will conduct electricity. Let the children try the others.

Follow-up
● Make sets of the objects that do and do not conduct electricity. What do they have in common?
● Ask the children to hunt around the classroom for other objects that they think will conduct electricity.

Questions
Why do the children think the wires are covered in plastic?
Why do they think it is so important not to touch the mains electricity points or electrical equipment at home?

AT1, AT3 (i), AT4 (i)

Electrical toys

Objective
To explore electricity and apply it to designing and making toys.

What you need
Electricity kits, junk materials (especially boxes), sticky tape, adhesive, paints or felt-tipped pens, tissue- and coloured paper, switches.

What to do
Be sure to emphasise that children should *never* touch mains electrical points.

Give the children the equipment and the switches. Can they find out what the switches are and how they work? Unscrew the tops and look inside.

Use the electricity kits and the junk materials to make little houses with lights inside them, and to make robots or strange creatures with lights, noises and moving parts. The children could use the lightbulbs for eyes, the buzzers for 'voices' etc.

Follow-up
● Decorate the little houses, and give them more than one light. Try coloured tissue-paper over the windows, or fabric curtains.
● Ask the children to paint a picture of their house with the lights on. How will they show the brightness of the lights?
● Ask the children to give names and magic powers to each of the electrical creatures, and make up a story about them. Dramatise the story.

Questions
Where do we position the lights in our classrooms? Where do we put lights in our homes? Why?

AT1, AT4 (i/iii/iv) D&M

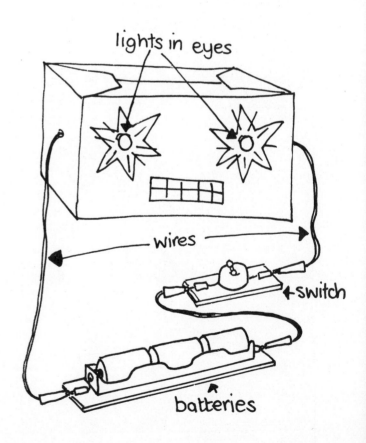

lights in eyes

wires

switch

batteries

Choice cards

Objective

To apply electricity in making a guessing game.

What you need

Electricity kit, card, aluminium foil, sticky tape, hole-punch.

What to do

Cut out some cards about 20cm by 15cm. Put words or numbers down one edge of each of the cards, and pictures to represent the words or numbers down the other edge, but in a random order so that each word is not opposite its relevant picture (see illustration).

Punch a hole beside each word, number and picture. On the reverse side, use folded strips of aluminium foil to join the hole by each picture with its relevant word or number, insulating each strip from the others with sticky tape.

Use the circuit with the wires touching the aluminium through the holes beside a word and its relevant picture. If the children get the answer right, the bulb will light.

Follow-up

● The 'choice cards' can be made to illustrate words or pictures to do with a class topic, to show a sequence of events, or any other ideas the children may have.
● A large version can be made for a parents' evening, for the parents to try and the children to explain.

Questions

Can the children explain to other people how the 'choice cards' were made and how they work?

AT1, AT4 (i) D&M

Magnets

Objectives

To experience the force of magnetism and the magnetic properties of different materials.

What you need

Strong magnets, a variety of objects and materials, both metal and non-metal, such as tin cans, glass jars, pencil, ruler, eraser, cork, coins, keys, paper-clips, paper plates.

What to do

Can the children discover which things are attracted to the magnets? Which ones are not?

How many paper-clips will each magnet hold?

What happens if you put the magnet ends near each other? Try with both ends.

Will magnetism go through paper plates? Put paper-clips on the plates and move the magnets underneath. Does magnetism work through a table?

Follow-up

• Make sets of the objects which were attracted, or not attracted, to the magnets.
• Try moving paper-clips by magnetism through other materials (leave all the magnetic equipment out for free play).
• Make a chart showing the strongest and weakest magnets.

Questions

How do the children think the magnets work? Why do they think some magnets are weaker than others?

What are the objects that get pulled toward the magnet made of?

AT1, AT3 (i), AT4 (i/iii)

Buried treasure

Objectives
To explore and apply magnetism.

What you need
Strong magnets, small metal objects eg steel washers, paper-clips, nuts and bolts; a sand tray with sand, a few non-metal objects such as buttons, corks etc.

What to do
Let the children bury the metal 'treasure' under the sand. Can they find it again?

Can they find the treasure without touching it with their fingers? Have the magnets visible and available, or suggest them. Hide the treasure and find it again.

If the children bury the non-metal 'treasure' how will they be able to find it without touching it with their fingers?

Follow-up
• Make a papier mâché 'Treasure Island' with 'treasure' buried on the island. Can the children show where the treasure is hidden by using magnets?
• Can they give instructions about finding the treasure?
• Older children could draw a map of the 'Treasure Island.'
• Find pictures of cranes with electromagnets in a car scrap-yard. Make models of these with construction kits or junk materials.
• Encourage the children to play with small metal toy cars or others, using magnets.

Questions
Can the children explain how they found the treasure?
Can they guess how magnetism works? (Any explanations.)

AT1, AT3 (i), AT4 (i) D&M

Magnetic forces

Objective
To explore and experience the force of magnetism.

What you need
Three or four strong disc magnets, a small magnet for suspending on cotton thread, a small ring holder (see illustration).

What to do
Put a strong disc magnet on the floor and cover with sugar paper. Suspend the swinging magnet above the disc so that there is a clearance of about 1 to 2cm above the disc, with room to swing. If you prepare this before the children come into the classroom, simply swing the magnet and ask the children to describe its movement. Can they guess why it is doing that?

   Put one disc over the ring post. Can the children predict what might happen if you put a second disc on top? Try putting attracting poles together using all the discs. Can the children separate them easily? Try putting repelling or 'like' poles together; the discs will remain in the air if they are strong enough. Can the children push them down? What can they feel?

Follow-up
• Write a poem or a story with the children about magic boots which stick to the ground or stay above the ground.
• Make up a dance sequence showing attraction and repulsion.

Questions
What did the magnetism feel like? Why must we be careful to keep strong magnets away from the computer or television?

AT1, AT4 (i)

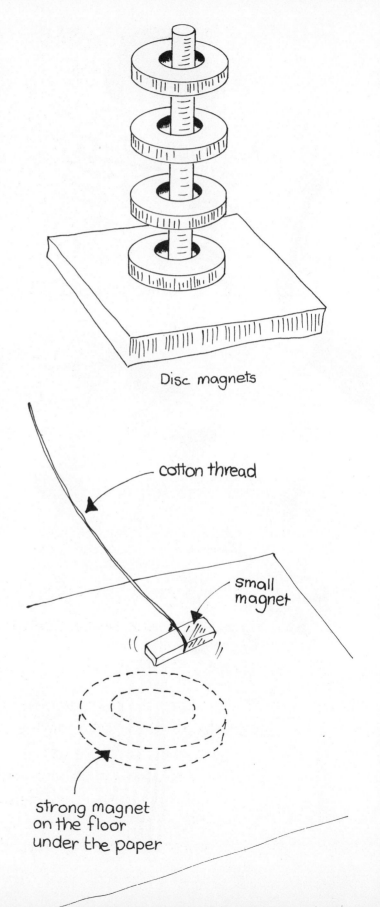

Disc magnets

cotton thread

small magnet

strong magnet on the floor under the paper

74

Making things move

Chapter eight

Without some force being exerted or some energy being transferred, stationary objects would not move and moving objects would not stop.

Activities using forces such as gravity, push and pull, air or water pressure, and different sorts of energy, will give the children opportunities to play, gain experience in making things move and discover ways of controlling their environment.

Using air pressure

Objective
To make things move by moving the air.

What you need
Tissue-paper, cylinder vacuum cleaner, a variety of small objects eg scrap paper, lentils, sand etc; dried peas, straws, saucers.

What to do
Hold a piece of paper near your face. Ask the children if they can think of ways of making the paper move without touching it. Try out their ideas, including blowing it. What made it move? Can you make it move in the opposite direction? Let them try with their own papers.

Bring out the vacuum cleaner and dismantle it. Discuss the different parts and reassemble it. (NB Remind the children not to touch electrical equipment without permission.)

Let the children spread the small objects about and take turns in making them move into the cleaner.

Follow-up
• Give the children the task of transferring dried peas from saucer to saucer with a straw. Older children could time themselves with a sand-timer.
• Investigate sucking speeds with milk or soft drinks.
• Find information and story books featuring vacuum cleaners.
• Make models of vacuum cleaners.

Questions
Which end of the cleaner sucks? Which end blows? Which seems to be stronger — blowing or sucking? Why do babies need to be strong suckers?

AT1, AT3 (i), AT4 (iii)

Fans

Objective
To make things move by moving the air.

What you need
Paper, sticky tape, crayons.

What to do
Put a little square of paper on the table. How can we make it move? Accept all the children's ideas and try them out if possible. Is there any other way of making the air move the paper without blowing or sucking it?

Show them how to make a fan and 'push' the air with it. Let them colour the paper, make fans and then use them in 'paper races'.

Follow-up
• Join up two or more fans along their sides to make bigger fans.
• Make a collection of commercial fans to display, and look at their shapes, sizes and materials.
• Make a giant Chinese fan and decorate it.

Questions
How far can the moving air push the paper? Does the paper always go straight? What does moving air feel like on our faces?

AT1, AT4 (iii) D&M

Windmills

Objective
To show how moving air can make things move and turn.

What you need
Paper, crayons, scissors, lengths of wood (eg old wooden rulers), nails, hammer, straws or small beads, sticky tape or adhesive.

What to do
Give the children pieces of paper about 12cm square, and ask them to colour them in. Make diagonal cuts towards the centre and fold alternate points into the centre, sticking each one down (see illustration). Make a hole in the centre large enough to allow the paper to rotate on the nail without coming off the nailhead. Attach the windmills to the wood with the nails, putting a small piece of straw (3 to 4mm) between the wood and the windmill to give clearance. Try pushing the windmills through the air in the classroom and outside in the wind.

Follow-up
- Visit a local windmill.
- Find information and story books featuring windmills eg *The Little Red Hen*.
- Make junk models of windmills.

Questions
Which way round does the windmill turn? Can they think of a way of making it revolve the other way round? (Older children might try making a second windmill with the opposite points folded in, or they may have other ideas.)

Can the children think of or find other objects that turn round?

AT1, AT4 (iii) D&M

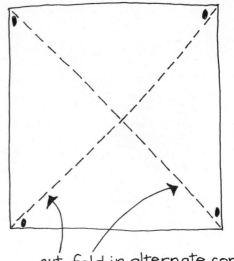

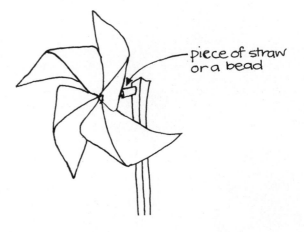

cut, fold in alternate corners

piece of straw or a bead

Hot air rising

Objective

To show how hot air rising can make things move.

What you need

Paper, crayons, scissors, strong cotton thread, access to a fan heater or hair drier.

What to do

Give the children circles of paper approximately 12cm in diameter. Colour in both sides. Help the children to cut the circle into a spiral. Fasten pieces of thread to the centre. Ask the children if they can think of ways of making the spirals move or spin – try out their ideas if possible.

Position the circles so that they hang freely near a heat source. Can the children guess what might be making them move now?

Follow-up

● Make a hot air balloon with a very large thin polythene bag (eg from a dry-cleaner) and hold the fan heater or hair drier underneath.
● Look at spiral springs and use them for printing.
● Read about Winnie-the-Pooh and the 'little cloud'.

Questions

Which way round do the spirals spin? Can the children think of ways of making them spin the other way?

What will feathers do if they are dropped near the heater?

Can the children think how the birds might use hot air currents?

AT1, AT4 (ii/iii)

Using water pressure

Objectives
To make air and water move, and use water to move other things.

What you need
Water pumps, water tank, bucket or bowl, siphon tubing, syringes to fit the tubing.

What to do
Let the children experiment with the pumps. What comes out of the pump with the first squeeze? What happens later? If the pump is valve-operated, can they see the valves moving? Can the pump work if they block the exit pipe?

Use the syringes in the water tank. Can the children find out how to get the air out to let the water in?

Make a hydraulic system by filling the siphon tubing with water and attaching a full and an empty syringe at the ends. Use it to push and pull.

Follow-up
• Investigate bicycle and balloon pumps.
• Show how to move water from a high tank to a low tank by siphoning (with the tubing full of water and the upper end under the surface of the 'high' water level).
• Find information books illustrating water and oil pumps.

Questions
How much 'push' do the children have to use on the pump? How much on the syringe?

Human beings have a kind of 'valve' in the back of their throats . . . can the children suggest what it might be used for?

AT1, AT4 (iii)

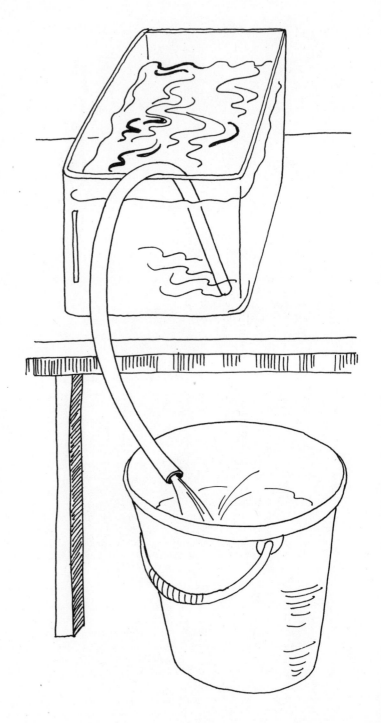

Sliding

Objectives

To use the force of gravity to make things move and slide, and give some experience of friction.

What you need

A ramp (a piece of wood approximately 1 metre long, 15cm or more wide, with a strip of wood attached across the back to hook over the horizontal bar of a chair or other item of furniture) or access to a slide; various flat and rounded objects.

What to do

Put a cereal packet on the floor. Does it move? Ask the children how they could make it move. Try out all their viable ideas. Raise the ramp to its support, and put the box on it. What will the box do now? Try it.

What other objects will move down the ramp? How will they move?

What about the children's shoes? Which ones will slide down? Look at the undersides of the shoes and discuss them. Try out the shoes, and the other objects. Sort out the ones that slide and the ones that roll.

Follow-up

● Make a 'cable-car' with string for the cable, yoghurt pots with string loops as the cars, and a paper-clip hook to the cable. Try these out with play people. Older children can make models of skiers in Plasticine, with lolly-stick skis and toothpicks for ski-sticks.

Questions

Do the objects still go down the ramp if you do not push them?
When do the objects stop moving?

AT1, AT3 (i), AT4 (iii) D&M

Wheels

Objective
To use wheels to investigate moving.

What you need
Toy cars, other vehicles made from classroom construction kits, a ramp (see previous activity), or access to a slide; objects of different shapes.

What to do
Play with the vehicles by rolling them across the floor. How far do they roll? Do they roll straight? Would they roll on the carpet? How far would they roll if placed on the ramp? Do they roll without a push? (It is difficult for children *not* to push them but you could show the difference by using a ruler as a 'starting gate' and simply lifting it up to release the car.)

Which shapes roll? What happens if you raise the ramp higher and roll things down?

Follow-up
• Make a large junk model of a bus with people's faces at the windows for the song 'The wheels on the bus go round and round'.
• Make junk models of things with pretend wheels.

Questions
What happens to moving cars if the ramp is nearly flat? What happens if it is very steep?

What happens if there is a doll in the car? Is there any way of stopping the doll from falling out?

AT1, AT3 (i), AT4 (iii)

Boats

Objective
To show how moving air can make things move on the water.

What you need
Waterproof junk materials, eg polystyrene trays, plastic pots, lids, straws; Plasticine, adhesive, sticky tape, paper, scissors, water tray, hole-punch.

What to do
Give the children paper squares (9 to 10cm) to colour in patterns. Make little sailing boats using these for sails by slotting a straw through and sticking them in the centre of the plastic tub boats with Plasticine.

Which way will the boats go if we blow them? What will happen if we blow on the other side?

Follow-up
● Try using straws and fans to blow the boats along.
● Make bigger sailing boats and try them outside on the tank or a pond.
● Find books and songs about boats.
● Make boats with pieces of wood and card or cloth sails.

Questions
How can you make your boat go where you want it to go?

What happens if you use a lot of 'blow'? What happens if you use very little?

AT1, AT3 (i), AT4 (iii) D&M

Pushing and pulling

Objective
To show how we can make things move by pushing, pulling and squeezing.

What you need
Big strong grocery boxes, string or rope, empty squeezy bottles, water.

What to do
Ask a child to sit in a box. How can we make the box move with her in it? How much push or pull will be needed? One person to push or two? Try it.

What if a rope is fastened to the box? Can the children think of ways of making the box slide more easily on the floor?

Try 'squeeze-power' out in the playground with plastic bottles full of water. Which is stronger — one hand or two?

Follow-up
• Decorate the big boxes to make them into vehicles for free play.
• In PE do movements involving pushing and pulling with hands, backs, and feet. Can the children pull things with their feet?

Questions
What makes us strong enough to push and pull? What do the children think helps us to be strong and healthy?

AT1, AT4 (iii) D&M

Winding up

Objective
To use the energy from elastic bands to make things move.

What you need
One metre of elastic, elastic bands, old birthday cards, wind-up toys.

What to do
Double the elastic and fasten between two chairs horizontally. Put the card between the two sides of the elastic and twist it round a few times. What do the children think will happen if you let it go? Which way round will it go? Let them see and try for themselves. Can they make it go the other way?

Follow-up
• Fasten the elastic in a safe place for the children to play with, using coloured cards of their own to twist and turn.
• Give the children a few wind-up toys to play with, and measure the distance travelled etc.
• Make a collection of wind-up toys to display.
• In PE and movement lessons, explore twisting, turning and 'elasticity'.

Questions
Can the children think of other things that are wound up, or that have elastic in them? Would it be the same if we used string instead of elastic?

AT1, AT4 (iii)

Throwing

Objective
To use our energy to make things move by throwing them.

What you need
Paper, felt-tipped pens, paper plates, balls, bean bags.

What to do
Hold a paper plate in the air. Let it drop. What does it do? Can the children think of ways of making the paper plate fly across the room. (NB Remind them of the importance of not throwing things *at* people.) Try out their ideas. How far do the paper plates go? How high do they go?

Try the same with a piece of paper, then help them to fold it into a simple paper plane. Measure with strides or footsteps how far they go inside and outside.

Follow-up
• Let the children decorate their planes and flying saucers with felt-tipped pens.
• Make a chart showing the highest and farthest flights.
• Write a class poem about flying.
• Visit a museum displaying aircraft.
• Find information and story books about aircraft and flight.
• Use the balls and bean bags to practise and measure throwing.

Questions
Is it better to throw the plates the right way up or upside-down?
What happens if you throw the planes into the wind? Away from the wind?

AT1, AT4 (iii)

Nursery rhymes and stories

Chapter nine

The enjoyable familiarity of nursery rhymes and well-known stories makes them useful for giving confidence in language, action songs and art.

If used as starting points for designing and making things they will also give scope for:

- Investigating materials – card, paper, plastics, fabrics, adhesives, water and air.
- Investigating forces – gravity, air and water pressure, push and pull.
- Scientific language development – planning, predicting, questionning, describing and explaining.
- Developing mathematical skills and understanding – comparing, estimating and measuring length, height, pressure and weight.

Humpty Dumpty

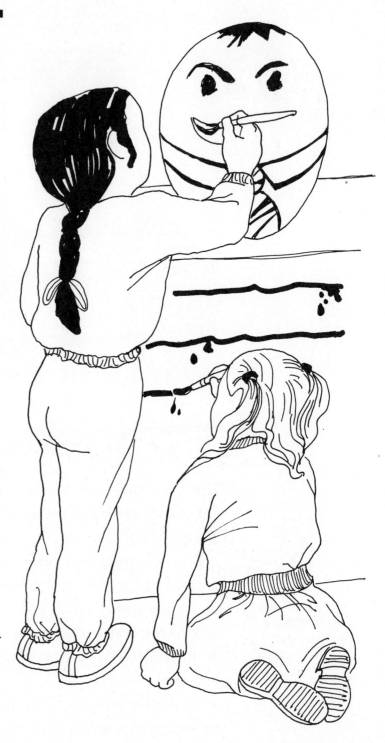

Objectives

To investigate structures and experience forces by making Humpty Dumpty and his wall.

What you need

Junk boxes of all sizes, adhesive, sticky tape, paint, large balloons, papier mâché, Plasticine, six eggs, trays for paint.

What to do

Cover two or three large balloons with papier mâché; dry and paint them as Humpty Dumpties. Give them extra stability if necessary by putting pieces of Plasticine inside when dry, and resealing.

Ask the children to use the junk boxes to make a wall strong enough for Humpty to sit on. How high will it be? How wide? Can they decorate it to make it look like a wall?

Follow-up

• Hard-boil three of the eggs. Have ready trays of medium-thick paint. Cover a table with newspaper and sugar paper. Can the children find out which eggs are raw and which are hard-boiled? Roll them in the paint and then across the paper. Can they guess now? Catch the eggs and roll them back. (Even the breakages are interesting!)

Questions

How did they make the boxes fit together in the wall? How did the raw eggs roll? What about the hard-boiled eggs? Why do they think that happens?

AT1, AT3 (i), AT4 (iii) D&M

Hickory Dickory Dock

Objectives

To explore materials and experience forces and energy by making a clock and a 'remote control' mouse.

What you need

Junk boxes, sticky tape and adhesive, card, paints, fabrics, scissors, string, paper-fasteners, other junk materials.

What to do

Look at the clock in the nursery rhyme book, and compare it with real ones. Can the children use the boxes to make a tall grandfather clock? Cut out and stick on a clock face, using the paper-fasteners to enable the hands to move.

Can the children use the fabrics to make little mice? Can they think of ways of making a mouse go up the clock without holding it? How will it get down again? (String? Elastic? Magnets? Other methods?)

Follow-up

● Tape record the song, with the children's percussion or the sound of the clock. Let the children play the tape and have goes at raising and lowering the mouse during free play periods.

Questions

Can the children explain how they made the clock and the mouse? What did they do to make the mouse go up? Can they think of an easier way to make a mouse go up a clock?

AT1, AT3 (i), AT4 (iii) D&M

Little Miss Muffet

Objectives
To investigate structures and patterns by making a spider and its web.

What you need
Wool (dark and crinkly if possible), fabric, pipe-cleaners, sticky tape.

What to do
If possible, find and visit a real spider's web and look at it and the spider. Can the children guess or see how many legs the spider has? Make little spiders with small pieces of fabric and four pipe-cleaners twisted around to make eight legs.

Let the children help you to construct a large woolly web, with spokes attached to floor, walls and ceilings, and a spiral woven from the centre outwards. Hang their spiders on the web.

Follow-up
• Find information and story books about spiders.
• Use the spiders for counting games.
• Use a screw top jar with milk to shake and convert into curds and whey.

Questions
Ask the children why a real spider's web is sticky.

Can they think of any other animals that might have eight legs? What about animals with two or four legs? Can they think of any animals with six or more legs?

Is there anything about a spider that makes them feel frightened?

AT1, AT2 (ii), AT4 (iii) D&M

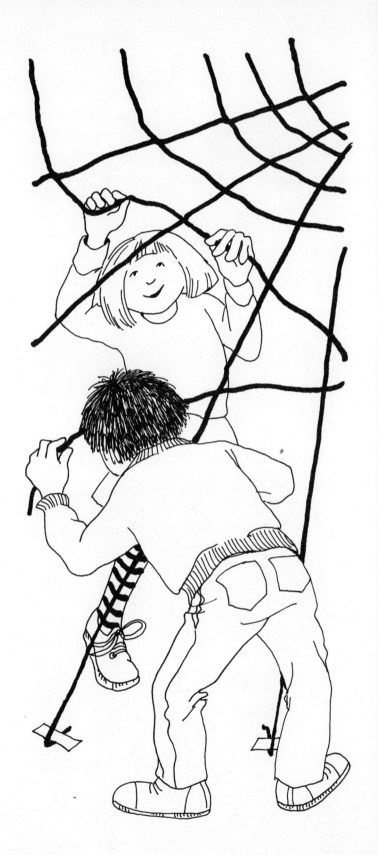

Jack and the beanstalk

Objectives
To investigate structures and forces by building a castle, and by making a free-standing beanstalk structure.

What you need
Grocery and cereal boxes, string, card, adhesive, sticky tape, scissors, coloured acetate film, newspaper, string, green crêpe or tissue-paper.

What to do
Can the children use the boxes to make a giant castle big enough to sit inside? What about doorways? Can they think of a way to use the card to make a roof?

Help them where necessary to build the castle and roof. Fill any gaps with coloured acetate film to add colour and mystery to the castle interior.

Ask older children to try to use the newspaper to make a free-standing beanstalk as tall as possible for Jack to climb. How can they make the floppy newspaper strong enough to stay upright? Use the green paper to decorate the beanstalk.

Follow-up
● Use the castle and the beanstalk for measuring activities.
● Add red paper flowers and green beans to the beanstalk.
● Paint pictures of castles.
● Dramatise the story of Jack.

Questions
Can the children explain to someone else how they built the structures? Which are the strongest and weakest parts of the castle? How do real beanstalks growing in the garden manage to stay upright?

AT1, AT3 (i), AT4 (iv) D&M

The three bears

Objectives

To explore materials and experience forces by designing and making the three bears' beds.

What you need

Grocery and cereal packets, adhesive, sticky tape, three different-sized teddy bears, a doll to be Goldilocks, card, paint, fabrics, scissors.

What to do

Let the children choose boxes to fit the three bears and cut the boxes, if necessary, to make them into beds. Can the children suggest ways of raising the beds off the ground? Follow up their ideas.

   Use the card to make headboards with names on. Paint the beds and use the fabrics to make sheets and pillows (stuffed with fabric or old tights).

Follow-up

• Ask the children if they can use the junk materials to make bunk beds for the dolls in the home corner.
• Make sets of children who sleep in single beds and in bunk beds.
• Use percussion with the song 'When Goldilocks went to the house of the bears'.
• For six-year-olds: can they suggest ways of making a bed or chair that will collapse when Goldilocks sits on it?

Questions

How did the children know which box was the right size for each teddy? Are their beds at home raised off the ground?

AT1, AT3 (i), AT4 (iii) D&M

The three little pigs

Objectives

To explore materials and forces by making the three little pigs' houses.

What you need

Balloons, papier mâché, art straws or similar, tissue-paper, sticky tape, twigs, wooden bricks, junk materials, string, paint.

What to do

Use the papier mâché on the balloons to make some pigs, and paint when dry.

Can the children make three houses for the pigs using the materials? Which materials will they use for each one?

Help them to make a house with the straws and tissue-paper that will blow down with huffing and puffing (eg straw squares covered with tissue-paper, joined together). Practise blowing it down.

Follow-up

• Can the children make a wall with cereal packets strong enough to stay up when you throw a soft sponge ball at it?
• Use the children's ideas to make more balloon animals — from the whole balloon shape or cut in half (eg tortoises, giant ladybirds).
• Dramatise the story of the three little pigs.

Questions

What seems to make the straw house move?

Can the children see the air from the huffing and puffing?

What else can they make move by their huffing and puffing? (NB Safety with asthmatics!) What are their own houses built of?

AT1, AT3 (i), AT4 (iii) D&M

Noah's ark

Objectives
To explore materials, forces and absorbency by making boats.

What you need
Water tank, toy farm animals, junk materials (especially waterproof ones), adhesive, sticky tape, small boxes.

What to do
Read and sing about Noah's ark. Show the children the toy animals. Can they make boats that will float on the water and keep the animals dry?

Where is the best place for the animals to be in the boat?

Follow-up
• Can the children make a cabin in the boat so that the animals can stay dry even if it rains?
• Choose percussion instruments to go with the song, representing the rain, the animals, the rainbow. Tape record the song.
• Make a collection of toy boats to investigate and display.

Questions
Why did the children choose those materials to make their boats? Can they think of other things that might float?

Where did they have to put the animals to keep the boat steady?

AT1, AT3 (i), AT4 (iii) D&M

Resources

Sticking and painting

Acrylics
Adhesive
Adhesive sticks
Brushes
Charcoal
Crayons
Diffusers
Elastic bands
Eye-droppers
Fingers!
Inks
Masking tape
Paper-clips
Paper-fasteners
Pencils
Powder paint
Sponges
Spoons
Stapler
Sticky tape
Straws
String
Syringes
Wallpaper paste
Wool

Papers

Acetate film
Aluminium foil
Blotting paper
Card (all colours)
Coloured foil
Corrugated card
Crêpe paper
Frieze paper
Kitchen paper
Sugar paper
Tissue-paper

Containers

Babyfood jars
Bowls
Buckets
Jam jars
Junk boxes — all sorts
Margarine tubs
Plastic lemonade
   bottles
Plastic sweet jars
Saucers
Squeezy bottles
Tins
Trays
Yoghurt pots

Other useful items

Audio tape
Clay
Cotton thread
Freezer
Home corner equipment
Musical instruments
Oven
Overhead projector
Plasticine
Refrigerator
Sand tray and equipment
Tools for working with wood,
   clay and dough
Toy animals, vehicles etc
Water tray and equipment
Wood

Science equipment

Balloons
Beans, peas,
   seeds etc
Bubble solution
   (see page 43)
Clocks
Construction toys
Electricity kits
Eye-droppers
Fabrics
Feathers
Funnels
Insect viewers
Junk
Kaleidoscope
Lenses
Magnets (strong)
Mechanical toys
Metal objects
Mirrors
Nails
Plaster of Paris
Plunger
Prisms
Pumps
Ramp
Salt
Sand-timers
Saucepan
Springs
Sugar
Syringes
Tools (gardening
   and household)
Tubing
Water wheel

Other Scholastic books

Bright Ideas

The Bright Ideas books provide a wealth of resources for busy primary school teachers. There are now more than 20 titles published, providing clearly explained and illustrated ideas on topics ranging from *Word Games* and *Science* to *Display* and *Classroom Management*. Each book contains material which can be photocopied for use in the classroom.

Teacher Handbooks

The Teacher Handbooks give an overview of the latest research in primary education, and show how it can be put into practice in the classroom. Covering all the core areas of the curriculum, the *Teacher Handbooks* are indispensable to the new teacher as a source of information and useful to the experienced teacher as a quick reference guide.

Management Books

The Management Books are designed to help teachers to organise their time, classroom and teaching more efficiently. The books deal with topical issues, such as *Parents and Schools* and organising and planning *Project Teaching*, and are written by authors with lots of practical advice and experiences to share.

Let's Investigate

Let's Investigate is an exciting range of photocopiable activity books giving open-ended investigative tasks. Designed to cover the 6 to 12-year-old range these books are ideal for small group or individual work. Each book presents progressively more difficult concepts and many of the activities can be adapted for use throughout the primary school. Detailed teacher's notes outlining the objectives of each photocopiable sheet and suggesting follow-up activities have been included.